WARNING!
A spell is about to be cast on you—
    You'll fall for this <u>cantankerous little
witch in the striped socks and bent hat</u>—
and you'll love <u>her eccentric friends</u>:
Gaylord, the intellectual buzzard,
<u>Irwin, the shy and shaggy troll,</u> and
<u>The Grelber, the master of insult.</u>

I LOVE YOU,

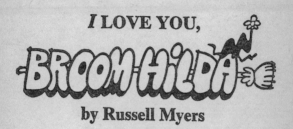

by Russell Myers

tempo
books

GROSSET & DUNLAP, INC.
A National General Company

Publishers   **New York**

Copyright © 1973 The Chicago Tribune
All Rights Reserved
ISBN: 0-448-05593-7
Tempo Books is Registered in the U.S. Patent Office
A Tempo Books Original
Published Simultaneously in Canada

Printed in the United States of America

5/34

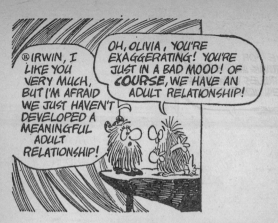

RUSSELL MYERS

PHOOEY.... THREE YEARS OF ANALYSIS AND I **STILL** DON'T KNOW WHO I AM!

5/12

CRUNCH
CHEW
MUNCH

RUSSELL MYERS

© 1972 by The Chicago Tribune
World Rights Reserved

RUSSELL MYERS

RUSSELL MYERS

© 1972 by The Chicago Tribune
World Rights Reserved!

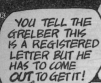

© 1972 by The Chicago Tribune
World Rights Reserved

RUSSELL MYERS

THIS IS SURE WEIRD
SUNTAN LOTION... IT'S AS
THICK AS HONEY!

RUSSELLMYERS

WHO GOT
MY HONEY
?

© 1975 by The Chicago Tribune
World Rights Reserved

1/6

© 1973 by The Chicago Tribune
World Rights Reserved

APPARENTLY AT THE AGE OF 1500 YOU HAVE ONLY ENOUGH ADRENALINE TO BE FRIGHTENED IN SLOW MOTION!

1/30

RUSSELL MYERS

2/2

RUSSELL MYERS

IT'S OVER! THE FOOTBALL SEASON IS OVER! I CAN'T BELIEVE IT'S GONE!

1-15

NO MORE MONDAY NIGHT FOOTBALL FOR SEVEN MONTHS! WHAT WILL I **DO**? I WON'T BE ABLE TO MAKE IT!

GASP

WHAT'S WRONG WITH HER?

SSH...

RUSSELL MYERS

FOR QUITE SOME TIME SHE'S HAD A TERIFFIC CRUSH ON HOWARD COSELL!

CON-TIN-UED

SELF-IMPROVEMENT MIGHT BE IN ORDER TODAY...

THE ANCIENT GREEK, DEMOSTHENES, PLACED PEBBLES IN HIS MOUTH AND SHOUTED OVER THE OCEAN'S ROAR, THEREBY IMPROVING HIS DICTION.

I'LL TRY THAT.

MUMPH GLUB NERDLE GLOOP FERMIN WONDLE OOG GNUF

RUSSELL MYERS

AS NEARLY AS I CAN DETERMINE I JUST PROPOSED TO A CARP!

RUSSELL MYERS

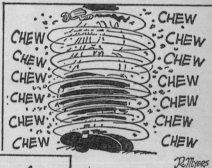

RUSSELL MYERS

RUSSELL MYERS

WHY ARE YOU DOING THAT?

I'VE GOT A DATE WITH A PORCUPINE!

RUSSELL MYERS

RUSSELL MYERS

© 1972 by The Chicago Tribune
World Rights Reserved

GLUG
GLUG

BURP BURP

BURP

BURP

RUSSELL MYERS

TROLLS AND COWS
HAVE FOUR STOMACHS.

I KNOW HOW TROUBLE-PRONE YOU ARE, SO EACH AND EVERY NIGHT I SAY A PRAYER FOR YOU...

I ALWAYS ASK THAT YOU BE KEPT SAFE FROM HARM THE FOLLOWING DAY...

THUD

I ALWAYS PRAY LATE AT NIGHT BECAUSE THAT'S WHEN THE AIR IS RIGHT AND PRAYERS GO STRAIGHT UP.

LAST NIGHT THERE WAS A HEAVY CLOUD COVER!